PARADES

Senior Author
William K. Durr

Senior Coordinating Author
John J. Pikulski

Coordinating Authors
Rita M. Bean
J. David Cooper
Nicholas A. Glaser
M. Jean Greenlaw
Hugh Schoephoerster

Authors
Mary Lou Alsin
Kathryn Au
Rosalinda B. Barrera
Joseph E. Brzeinski
Ruth P. Bunyan

Jacqueline C. Comas
Frank X. Estrada
Robert L. Hillerich
Timothy G. Johnson
Pamela A. Mason

HOUGHTON MIFFLIN COMPANY   BOSTON

Atlanta   Dallas   Geneva, Illinois   Lawrenceville, New Jersey   Palo Alto   Toronto

Acknowledgments

For each of the selections listed below, grateful acknowledgment is made for permission to adapt and/or reprint original or copyrighted material, as follows:

"Dogs," from *Around and About,* by Marchette Chute. Copyright © 1957. Reprinted by permission of the author.

"Doghouse for Sale," from *Doghouse for Sale,* by Donna Lugg Pape. Copyright © 1979 by Donna Lugg Pape. Reprinted with the permission of Garrard Publishing Co., Champaign, Illinois.

"Ducks," from *Nuts to You and Nuts to Me,* by Mary Ann Hoberman. Copyright © 1974 by Mary Ann Hoberman. Reprinted by permission of Russell & Volkening, Inc. as agents for the author.

"Here Comes the Band," by William Cole. Copyright © 1960 by William Cole. Reprinted by permission of the author.

"The Hungry Fox," an adaptation of text of *The Hungry Fox and the Foxy Duck,* copyright © 1978 by Kathleen Leverich. A Parents Magazine Press Book. Reprinted by permission of E. P. Dutton, Inc. and William Heinemann Ltd.

Continued on page 220.

Printed in the U.S.A.
ISBN: 0-395-37603-3
EFGHIJ-D-943210/8987

Contents

Magazine Two

Magazine Three

Parades
Magazine One

Contents

Stories

Article

Poems

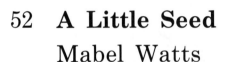

Skill: Quotation Marks

Vocabulary

A Good Place to Play

by James Marshall

Some friends need a place to play.
Will they find one?

Dog: Stop! Stop that playing!

Cat: We can't stop playing, Dog.
We are going to be in a show.

Turtle: The show is tomorrow, Dog.
We want to be good.
So we have to play today.

Dog: That may be so.
      But I'm trying to sleep!

Rabbit: It's daytime, Dog.
      Why don't you sleep at night?

Dog: I have to work at night.

Cat: OK, Dog.
      We'll go so that you can sleep.

Rabbit: Where will we go?
      We have so much to do.
      And we don't have much time!

Turtle: I didn't think I would make it.
But this is a good place to play.

Cat: We can play all day and night!

Rabbit: We'll be so good tomorrow.
We'll be the best in the show.

Bear: Oh, no you will not!
I'm going to be the best.

Cat: We didn't see you, Bear!
What are you doing up here?

Bear: I have come here to sing.
And I can't sing when you play.
Please take your things and go.

Turtle: Some bears are no fun at all!

17

Hen: Cat! Turtle! Rabbit!
What a show we'll have tomorrow!

Cat: We can't be in the show, Hen.
We wouldn't be any good.

Rabbit: We didn't find a place to play.

Hen: Come with me, my friends.
I have a good place to play.
I'm on my way there now.

Cat: Now we can play all we want.

Rabbit: We'll be the best in the show!

Turtle: Things are looking up!

Thinking It Over

Comprehension Questions

1. How did the friends find a place?
2. Why did the friends need to play?
3. Why didn't Dog want any playing?
   Tell why Bear didn't want any playing.
   Did Fox want the friends to play?
   Why not?

Word Watch

I _____ at _____.
   night   sleep

The kite is _____ _____ there.
   way   up

That _____ is _____ much fun!
   so   dog

I'm in a Show

The friends will play in a show.
Tell what you would do in a show.

Here Comes the Band

by William Cole

The band comes booming
down the street,
The tuba oomphs,
the flutes tweet tweet;
The trombones slide,
the trumpets blare,
The baton twirls up in the air.
There are "ooh's!" and "ah's!"
and cheers and
clapping —
And I can't stop
my feet from tapping.

Alma's Idea

by Ann Míranda with María Guerrero

Alma needs a place to play.
Find out how she gets a place.

Lupe: You can't play in here, Alma!

Alma: Why not, Lupe?
This is my room, too.
Clara and I want
to play school.

Lupe: My friends and I
are playing in here now.
You and Clara are too little
to play with us.

Clara: We can play out here, Alma.

Alma: This isn't the best place
to play school, Clara.
But it will have to do.
Come on, let me see your book.
I'll help you to read a story.

Clara: Alma, look at this house.
It's in a tree!

Alma: That's a tree house, Clara.

Clara: It would be nice to have
a tree house.

Alma: Yes, it would be nice.
Then we would have
a place to play!

Clara: How can we have a tree house
when we don't have a tree?

Alma: I think I have an idea.

Clara: Show me your idea, Alma.

Alma: OK. What do you think?

Clara: It isn't like the tree house
in the story.
But it is a tree house!

Alma: I think my dad can help us.
I'll ask Dad now.

Alma: Dad, we need a place to play.
I have an idea for a tree house.
Would you help us make it?

Dad: I can help make the house,
but how can I make the tree?

Alma: Please look at my idea.
I think Mother can help us
with it, too.

Dad: It's a good idea, Alma!
Let's ask Mother now.

Alma: I want a tree house, Mother.
Dad is going to make the house.
Will you help make the tree?

Mother: How can we make a tree?

Dad: Take a look at Alma's idea.

Mother: Oh, now I see how.
Let's get to work.

Lupe: What's going on down there?

Alma: I need a place to play.
So Mother and Dad are helping me
to make a tree house!

Lupe: A tree house?
You can't make a tree house
without a tree.

Alma: Take a look at this!

Lupe: It *is* a tree house!

What a good idea, Alma.

Now when I play in our room,
you'll have a place to play.

Then when you want our room,
I'll play down here.

Alma: What a good idea, Lupe!

Thinking It Over

Comprehension Questions

1. How did Alma get a place to play?
2. Why wouldn't Lupe let Alma and Clara play in the room?
3. Where did Alma get the idea for the tree house?

Word Watch

You can go into a **house.**
Name one more place
that you can go into.

You can find books at **school.**
Name one more thing that you
can find at school.

You can play in your **room.**
Name one more place to play.

My Place

    Do you have an idea for a place
that you would like to make?
    Tell what your idea is.

What Did They Say?

> I will help.
> I will.
> I will.

What did Hen say?
How can you tell she said it?

 I will help you, Rabbit.

 I would like help, Bear.

What did Bear say?
How can you tell he said it?

What did Rabbit say?
How can you tell he said it?

Alma: This is my room, too.

How can you tell that Alma
said this?
The word **Alma** tells you.

Alma said, "This is my room, too."

How can you tell that Alma
said this?
The words **Alma said** tell you.

"This is my room, too," said Alma.

Now how can you tell that Alma
said this?
The words **said Alma** tell you.

Now read this story.

Ben said, "Look at my rabbit."

Amy said, "Oh, I like it."

"Can that rabbit help you
to swim?" asked Amy.

Ben said, "I'll make
the rabbit big.
Then it will help me to swim."

"Isn't that rabbit too big?"
asked Amy.

"It isn't too big," said Ben.
"I like big, big rabbits."

Ben said, "Oh, no!
What will we do now?"

"It's OK," said Amy.
"My turtle can help us to swim.
But I will not make my turtle
too big!"

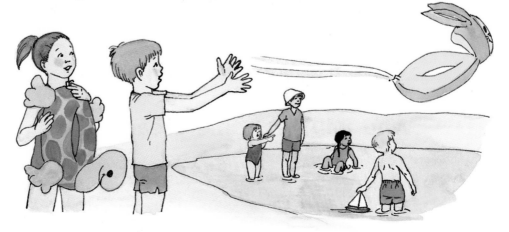

The Little Red Hen

Little Red Hen is going
to make bread.
Who will get some bread?

One day the little red hen said,
"Come see what I have!
I have some wheat.
I am going to plant it."

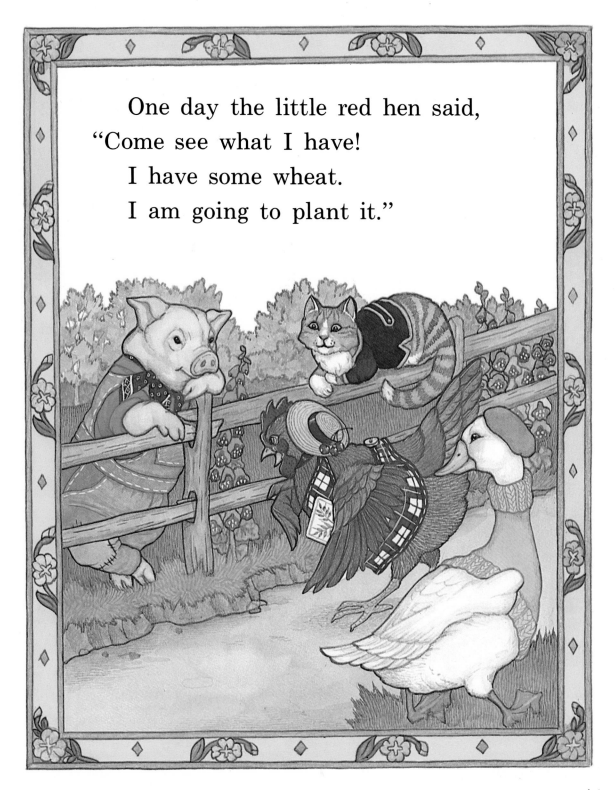

"Who will help me plant the wheat?" asked the little red hen.

"Not I," said the duck.

"Not I," said the cat.

"Not I," said the pig.

"Then I will plant it myself," said the little red hen.
And she did.

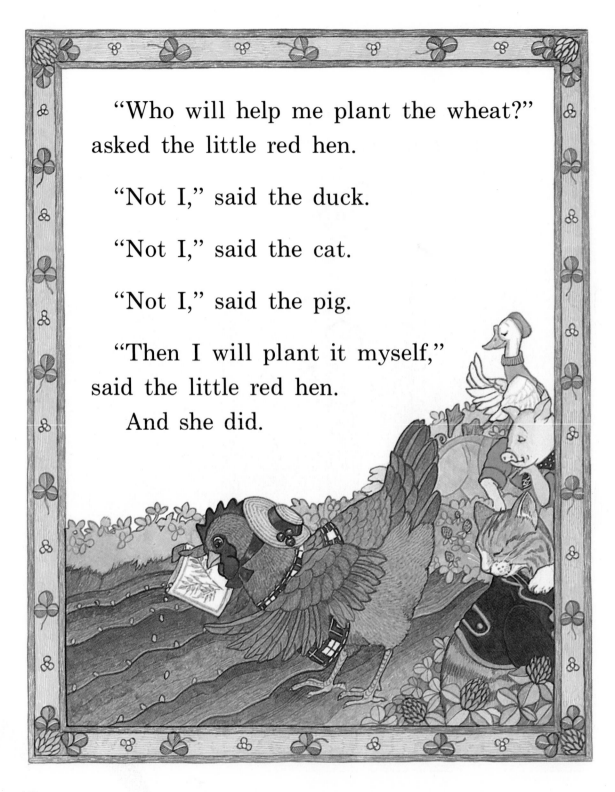

The wheat grew and grew.
It grew into a big plant.

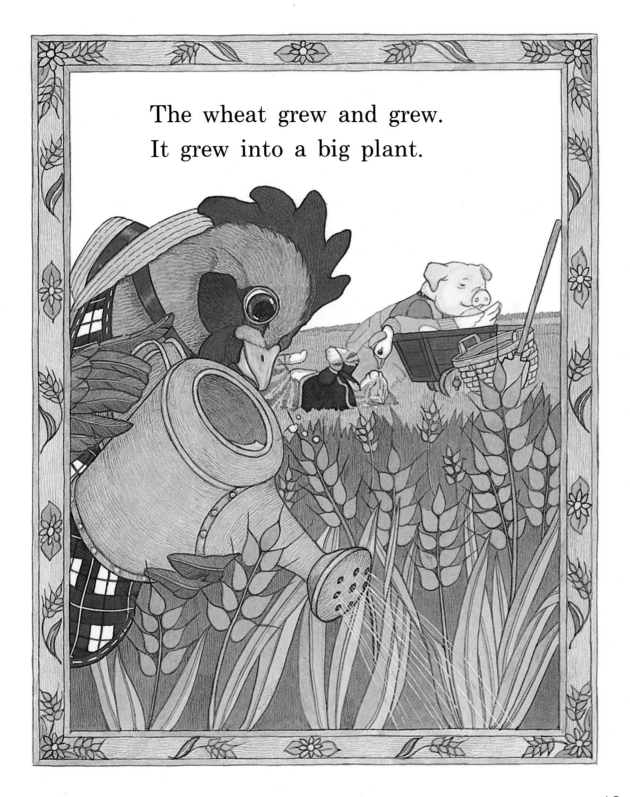

"Who will help me cut the wheat?" asked the little red hen.

"Not I," said the duck.

"Not I," said the cat.

"Not I," said the pig.

"Well then, I will cut it myself," said the little red hen.
And she did.

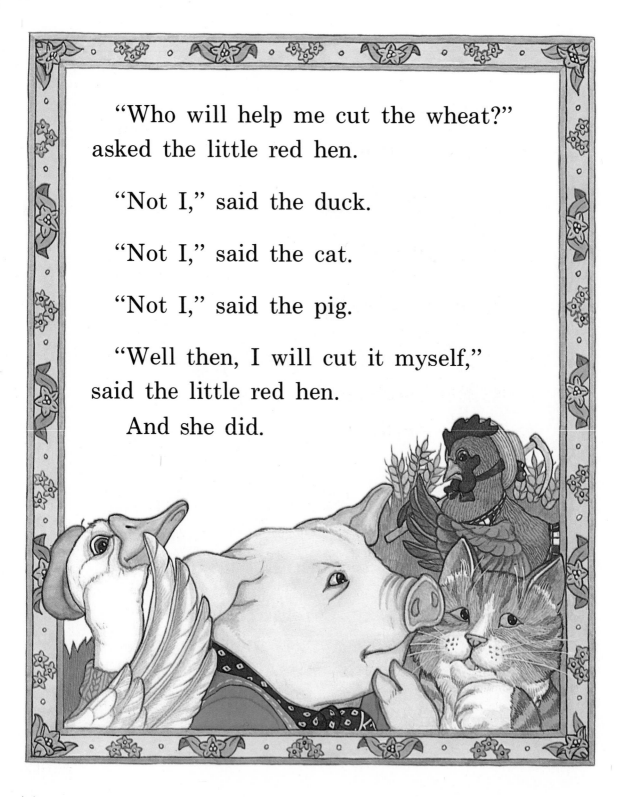

"Who will help me pound the wheat?" asked the little red hen.

"Not I," said the duck.

"Not I," said the cat.

"Not I," said the pig.

"Well then, I will pound it myself," said the little red hen.
And she did.

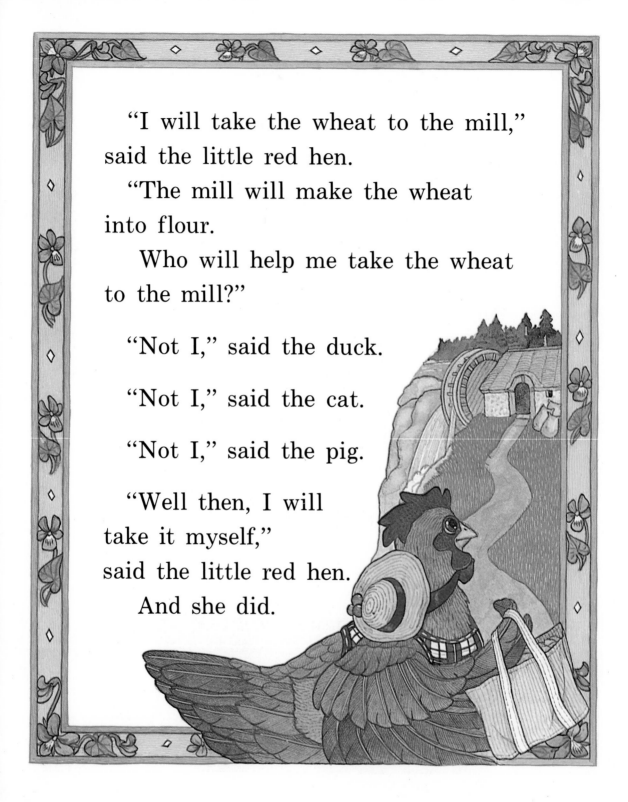

"I will take the wheat to the mill," said the little red hen.

"The mill will make the wheat into flour.

Who will help me take the wheat to the mill?"

"Not I," said the duck.

"Not I," said the cat.

"Not I," said the pig.

"Well then, I will take it myself," said the little red hen.
And she did.

"I will make bread with the flour," said the little red hen.

"Who will help me make the bread?"

"Not I," said the duck.

"Not I," said the cat.

"Not I," said the pig.

"Then I will make the bread myself," said the little red hen.

And she did.

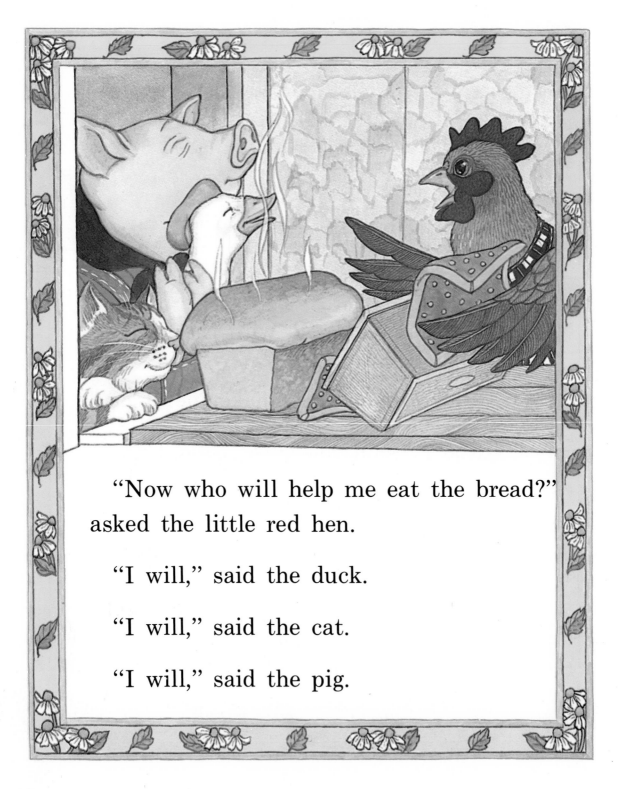

"Now who will help me eat the bread?" asked the little red hen.

"I will," said the duck.

"I will," said the cat.

"I will," said the pig.

"Oh, no," said the little red hen.

"You did not help me plant the wheat.

You did not help me cut the wheat.

You did not help me pound the wheat.

You did not help me take the wheat to the mill.

You did not help me make the bread, so you will not help me eat the bread.

I am going to eat it myself."

And she did.

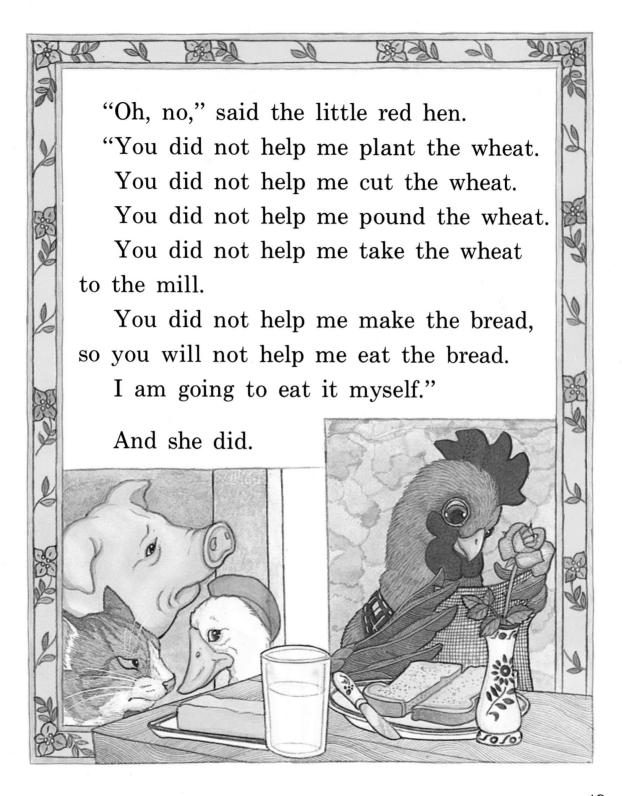

Comprehension Questions

1. Who was the one to get some bread?
2. Tell what Little Red Hen did to the wheat to make bread.
3. Why do you think no one would help Little Red Hen?

Word Watch

rabbit   duck   frog   fox   pig
turtle   bear   hen   cat

What do the words name?
Tell about the one that you
like best.

Show How the Wheat Grew

Little Red Hen planted wheat.
The wheat grew and grew.
Make some pictures to show how
the wheat grew and grew.

A Little Seed

by Mabel Watts

A little seed
For me to sow...

A little earth
To make it grow...
A little hole,
A little pat...
A little wish,
And that is that.

A little sun,
A little shower...
A little while,
And then — a flower!

Pam and Lee Bake Bread

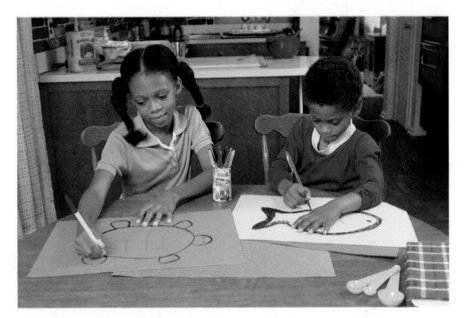

Pam and Lee are going
to make bread.

They can make the bread look
like a fish.

They can make it look like a bear.

Maybe they will make it look
like a turtle.

Let's see what Pam and Lee will do.

53

Pam and Lee mix some things
like this.

They need to mix the things
to make bread dough.

Then Pam and Lee mix the dough
like this.

Pam and Lee put the dough
in a good place.

They'll keep it there for some time.

Soon the dough will get big.

Now Pam and Lee work
with the dough.

Look, they have a turtle bread!

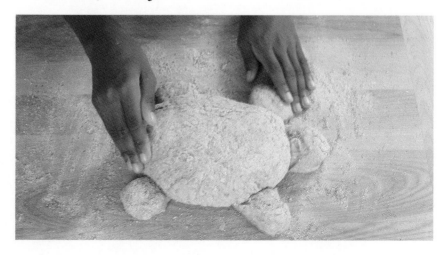

It's time to bake the bread.
Pam will put it in to bake.
Soon there will be bread to eat.

Now Pam will cut the bread,
and she and Lee will eat some.
They'll eat some now,
and keep the rest for tomorrow.

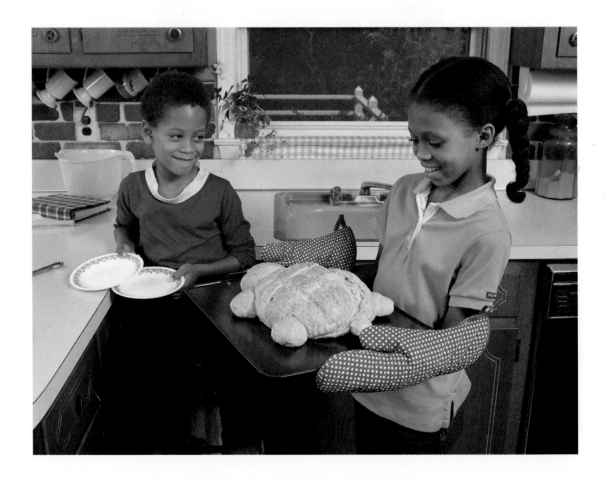

Comprehension Questions

1. What did Pam and Lee make the bread look like?
2. Why didn't Pam and Lee eat all the bread?

Word Watch

bake   mix   eat

The words tell about things to do. Which do you like to do best?

How Do You Bake Bread?

Tell about the things that Pam and Lee did to make bread.

Start with the mixing.

One More Thing, Dad

by Susan L. Thompson

Caleb is going for a walk.
Count the things Caleb will take
on the walk.

"I'm going out for a walk, Dad," Caleb said.

"Oh?" said Dad.

He was making bread.

"May I take a big orange with me?"
asked Caleb.

"There you are, Caleb," said Dad.
"There's an orange."

Caleb said, "That's 1."
He liked to count.

"Do you want something more?"
asked Dad.

"Maybe I'll take a sandwich, too,"
said Caleb.

"OK," said Dad.
"You can make it yourself."

Caleb liked making the sandwich.
Then he said, "That's 2."

"Some juice would be good
with this sandwich," said Caleb.

"Help yourself," said Dad.

"That's 3," Caleb counted.
"Now I'll get my lunch box," he said.

Caleb put the orange, the sandwich,
and the juice into the lunch box.
"This lunch box makes 4," he said.

"Now I'll need my jar," Caleb said.

"I think it's in your room," Dad said.

Caleb went to get the jar.
"It *was* there, Dad," said Caleb.
"That's 5," he counted.

"Now I'll need a coat," said Caleb.
"What do you think, Dad?"

Dad said, "Take your red coat."

Caleb went to get the red coat.
"6," he counted.
Then he said, "Maybe Obie
would like to come with me."

"Why not?" said Dad.
"Take Obie, too!"

"Obie! Come here, Obie," said Caleb.
"Obie makes 7," Caleb said to Dad.

Then Caleb went to get a kite.
"My kite will make 8," he said.
"And may I put on your hat, Dad?"

"It's yours!" said Dad, and he helped
Caleb put it on.

"9!" said Caleb.
"Now I have 9 things to take with me."

Caleb said, "I have an orange,
a sandwich, juice, my lunch box, my jar,
my coat, Obie, my kite, and your hat.
I think I have what I need.
I'm going out now."

"Have a good walk," Dad said.

But Caleb didn't go out.
He counted,
"1, 2, 3, 4, 5, 6, 7, 8, 9 ..."

"What is it, Caleb?" Dad asked.

"One more thing, Dad," said Caleb.
"Will *you* come for a walk with me?"

"Why, Caleb, I would like to go
with you!" said Dad.

"Then you make 10, big, big 10!"
said Caleb.
"1, 2, 3, 4, 5, 6, 7, 8, 9, 10!"

Comprehension Questions

1. What will Caleb take on the walk?
2. What do you think Caleb will do with all of the things?
3. Why do you think Caleb wanted to take Dad on the walk?

Word Watch

bread **a kite**

a coat **a jar**

What can you fly?

What can you eat?

What can you put on?

What can you put juice into?

Going for a Walk

Caleb wanted to take 10 things on the walk.

Tell what things you would take on a walk.

Magazine Wrap-up

What Happened?

1. Alma, Pam and Lee, and Caleb
   all made some things.
   Tell what things they made.

2. Cat, Turtle, and Rabbit looked
   for a place to play.
   What kind of playing did they do?
   Alma wanted a place to play, too.
   What kind of playing will she do?

Help!

Little Red Hen didn't get help when she needed it, but Alma did.

Tell about a time when someone helped you.

Books to Enjoy

Apple Tree! Apple Tree!
by Mary Blocksma

See what a good friend an apple tree can be.

Are You My Mother? by P. D. Eastman

A baby bird falls from his nest.
Can he find his mother?

Go Away, Dog by Joan L. Nödset

How will a dog make friends with a little boy?

Parades
Magazine Two

Contents

Stories

76

Doghouse for Sale

by Donna Lugg Pape

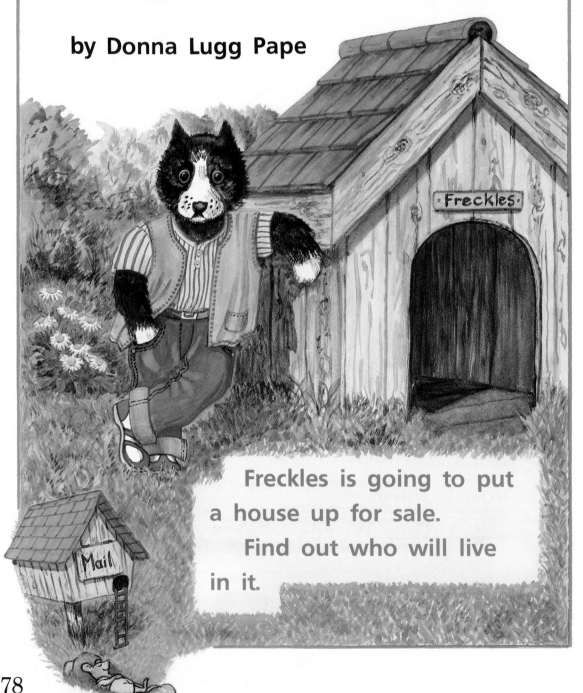

Freckles is going to put
a house up for sale.
Find out who will live
in it.

Freckles looked at his house.

"I don't want this house," he said.
"I will put this one up for sale."

Freckles put up a sign.

Dogs came to look at the house.
But no one wanted it.

"It needs paint," one dog said.

"Then I'll paint my house,"
said Freckles.
"I'll paint it red.
Then someone will want it."

Freckles went to the store
to get paint.

Then he went home.

Soon the house was painted red.
"That looks good," Freckles said.

Then Freckles put up a new sign.

Dogs came to look at the house.
But no one wanted it.

One dog said, "Your house needs
a new bed."

"I'll make a new bed for my house,"
said Freckles.

"Then someone will want it."

So Freckles went back to the store
to get what he needed to make a bed.

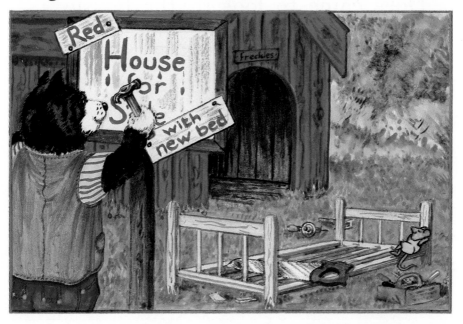

Soon the house had a new bed.

Freckles put up a new sign.

Dogs came to look at the house.
But no one wanted it.

One dog said, "It needs a window."

"I'll make a window for my house,"
said Freckles.
"Then someone will want it."

Freckles went back to the store.

Freckles worked hard.
Soon his house had a window.

Freckles put up a new sign.

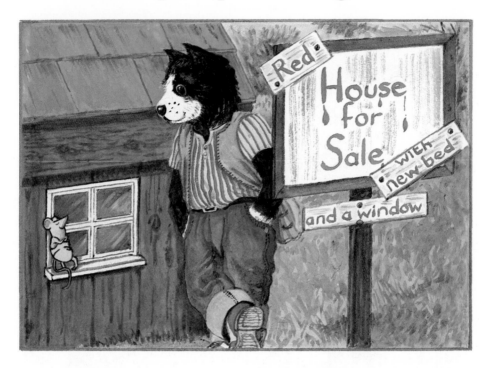

Dogs came to look at the house.
But no one wanted it.

"Your house needs trees around it,"
one dog said.

"Then I'll plant some," said Freckles.

Freckles went back to the store
to get some trees.

Soon the house had trees around it.

Freckles put up a new sign.

Dogs came to look at the house.
"We like your house," the dogs said.
"All it needs is a fence around it."

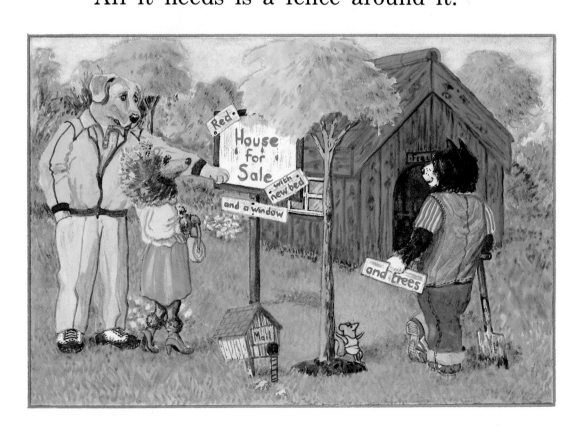

So Freckles went back to the store
to get a fence.

Then he went home and put
the fence around his house.

Freckles put up a new sign.

Dogs came to look at the house.

"This is a good house," one dog said.

"I want to live in it."

Freckles walked around his house.
He looked at the red paint.
He looked at the window.
He looked at all the trees.
He looked at the fence around it.

"This house is not for sale,"
Freckles said.
"I want to live in it myself."

And he did.

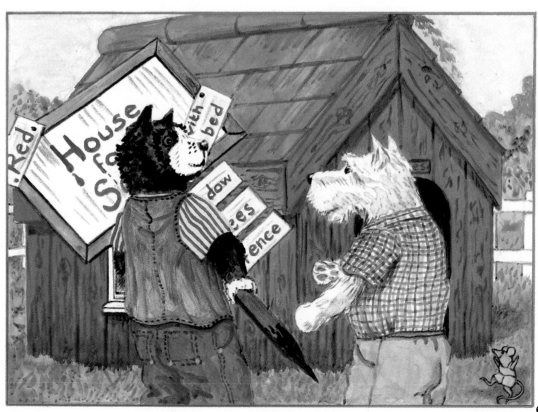

Thinking It Over

Comprehension Questions

1. Who will live in the house?
   Why did he want to live in it?
2. What things did Freckles do
   to the house?
3. Why did Freckles have to put up
   new signs?

Word Watch

**doghouse   storybook   catfish
homework   bedroom**

Draw pictures for the words.
Put the words with the pictures.

One More Thing, Freckles

Freckles did some things
to his house.

Think about one more thing
that Freckles can do.

Draw a picture showing how
the house would look.

Dogs

by Marchette Chute

The dogs I know
Have many shapes.
For some are big and tall,
    And some are long,
    And some are thin,
    And some
    are fat
    and small.

And some are little bits
    of fluff
And have no shape at all.

Signs All Around

There are signs all around you.
Some signs tell what to do,
while some signs tell what not to do.

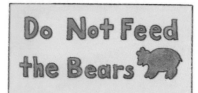

Signs can tell you that no one
is in.

Signs can tell you that something
is for sale.

Signs can help you find your way.
They can tell you which way to go.
Here are some street signs.

Let's say you want to go to New Street.
Which one of the street signs tells you
the way to go?

When you go for a walk,
you may see signs like these.
Some of the signs have words,
while other signs do not need words.
What do these signs tell you?

You can make signs to tell things.
You can make some signs
with words, and others without words.

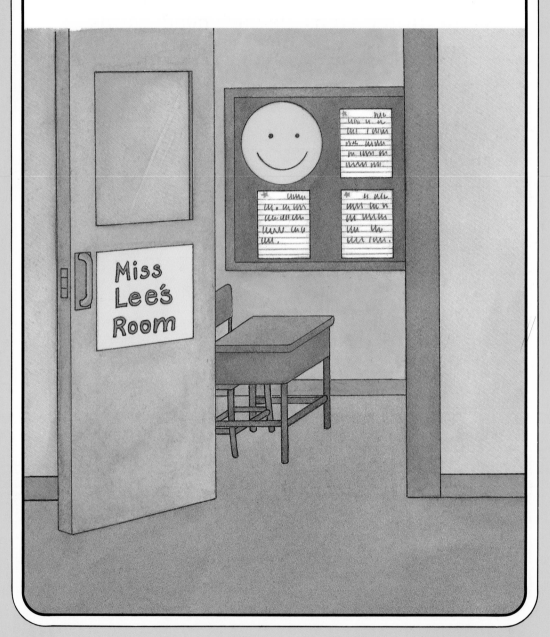

Thinking It Over

Comprehension Questions

1. What are some things that signs can tell you?
2. Why do you think some signs have words and not pictures?

Word Watch

No Fishing	Bread Baked Here	Orange Juice for Sale

Where would you see these signs?

Making Signs

Make two signs.
Make one sign with words.
Make one sign without words.

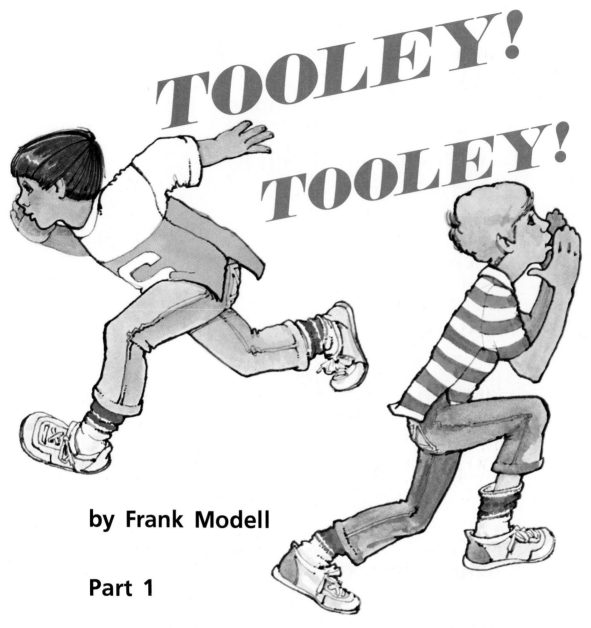

TOOLEY! TOOLEY!

by Frank Modell

Part 1

Marvin and Milton want to find
a brown dog.
See what they do to find the dog.

Marvin and Milton liked going
to the movies.

But on this day they had no money.

"Let's look around," said Marvin.
"Maybe we'll find some money."

Then Marvin said, "Look at
this sign."

NOW SHOWING

NEIGHBORHOOD NOTICES

For Sale
Boy's bicycle
24" wheel
Good Condition
call 463 2784

LOST DOG
Help find Tooley.
Tooley is my
brown dog.
Find Tooley
and I have
some money
for you.
Lisa Mills
call 463 5103

Firemen's Picnic
Come early
Saturday, Aug. 4
Valley
Everyone Welcome

97

"If we can find that dog, we'll have some money," said Marvin.

"I don't think we can find Tooley," said Milton.
"There are brown dogs all over the place."

"If I could fly, I could find Tooley,"
said Marvin.

"I would fly all over the place
and call for Tooley.

Tooley would look up and see me.

Then I would go down
and get Tooley."

"That's silly," said Milton.

"You don't like my ideas," said Marvin.

"I like your ideas when they aren't silly," said Milton.

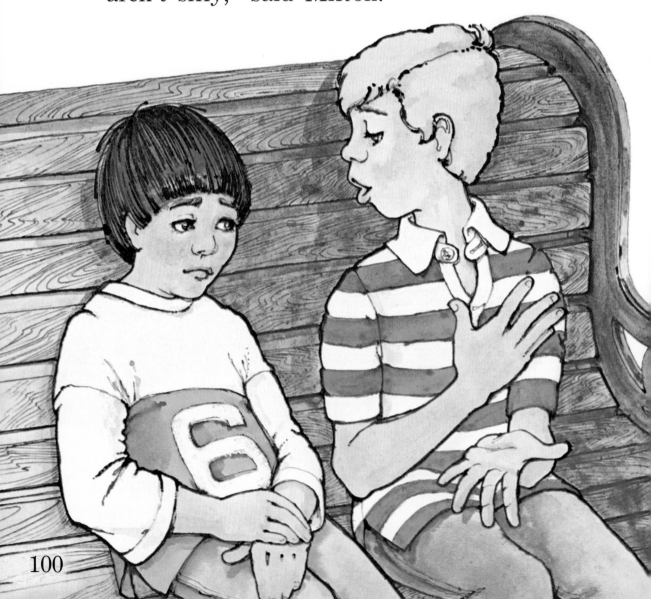

Then Marvin asked, "What if we
run up and down the street
and call for Tooley?

If I go this way, and you go
that way, one of us will find Tooley."

"We'll have to run," said Milton,
"if we want to see a movie."

So Marvin ran up the street
and Milton ran down the street.
They ran all around calling,
"Tooley! Tooley!"

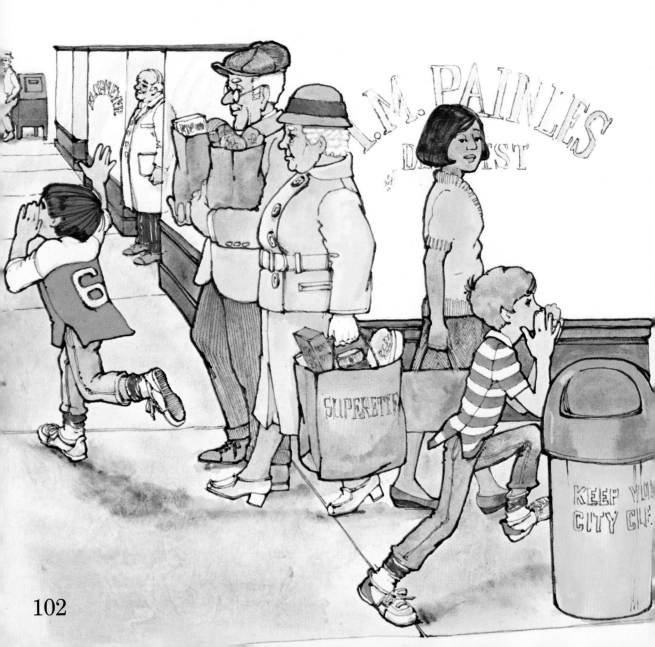

Thinking It Over

Comprehension Questions

1. What did Marvin and Milton do to find Tooley?
2. Which one of Marvin's ideas did Milton think was silly?

Word Watch

red   orange   brown

Draw a picture with red, orange, and brown in it.

Looking for Tooley

The boys called for Tooley.
Can you think of another way they could find Tooley?

TOOLEY! TOOLEY!

by Frank Modell

Part 2

Will Marvin and Milton find Tooley?
Will they have money for the movies?

Milton stopped and looked over
a fence.

There was a brown dog!

"Tooley?" asked Milton.
"You are Tooley, aren't you?
Tooley, I'm taking you home."

But then Milton saw a brown dog
on the street.

"I'll take him, too," Milton said.
"Maybe he is Tooley."

Marvin had found no dogs at all.
"If I were Tooley, where would
I go?" he asked himself.

Then it came to him.
"I would go
to Mr. Klopmeyer's store!"

"Mr. Klopmeyer," said Marvin,
"I'm looking for a dog."

"A hot dog?" asked Mr. Klopmeyer.

"No, not a hot dog!" said Marvin.
"That's silly!"

"Go take a look in the back,"
said Mr. Klopmeyer.
"You'll find some dogs out there."

Marvin looked at all the dogs.
"Tooley?" he asked.
A little brown dog ran up to him.

"You are Tooley!" said Marvin.
"Come on, Tooley.
We have to run.
You are going home."

"Tooley! Oh, Tooley!" said Lisa.
"Where were you?"

Marvin said, "I found him
at Mr. Klopmeyer's store."

Then Lisa said, "Thank you
for finding him.
This money is for you."

"Thanks," said Marvin.
"See you."

Then Marvin saw Milton running
down the street with some brown dogs.

"I found Tooley!" Milton called.

But then Milton saw that Marvin
had some money.

He could tell that Marvin
had found Tooley.

"I'll have to take back these dogs,"
Milton said.

"I'll help you," said Marvin.

"But we'll have to run all the way
if we want to get to the movies."

Comprehension Questions

1. Did Marvin and Milton get money
   for the movies? How?
2. How did Marvin know
   that Tooley would be
   at Mr. Klopmeyer's store?
3. Why did Milton have so many dogs
   with him?

Word Watch

orange   saw   sign

1. Which tree will she _____ down?
   We _____ a good movie.

2. Please _____ your name
   on the picture.
   The _____ tells us what is
   for sale.

3. Pam is eating an _____.
   I have an _____ hat.

A Pet Picture

Tooley was Lisa's pet.
Draw a picture of what you
would like for a pet.
Then show your picture and tell
why you would like to have that pet.

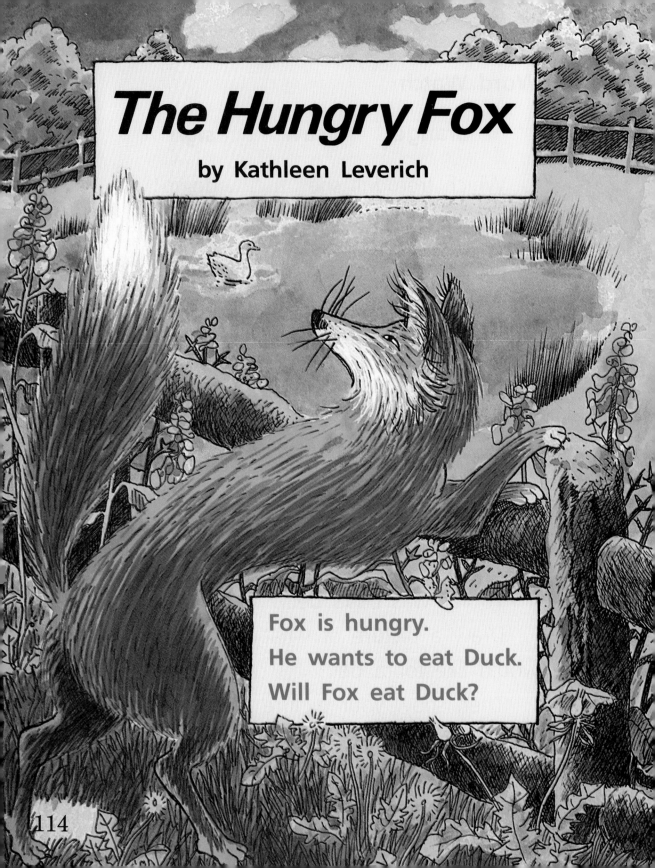

The Hungry Fox

by Kathleen Leverich

Fox is hungry.
He wants to eat Duck.
Will Fox eat Duck?

Once there was a smart little duck.
She lived on a pond.
The pond had a fence all around it.
It was good living on the pond.

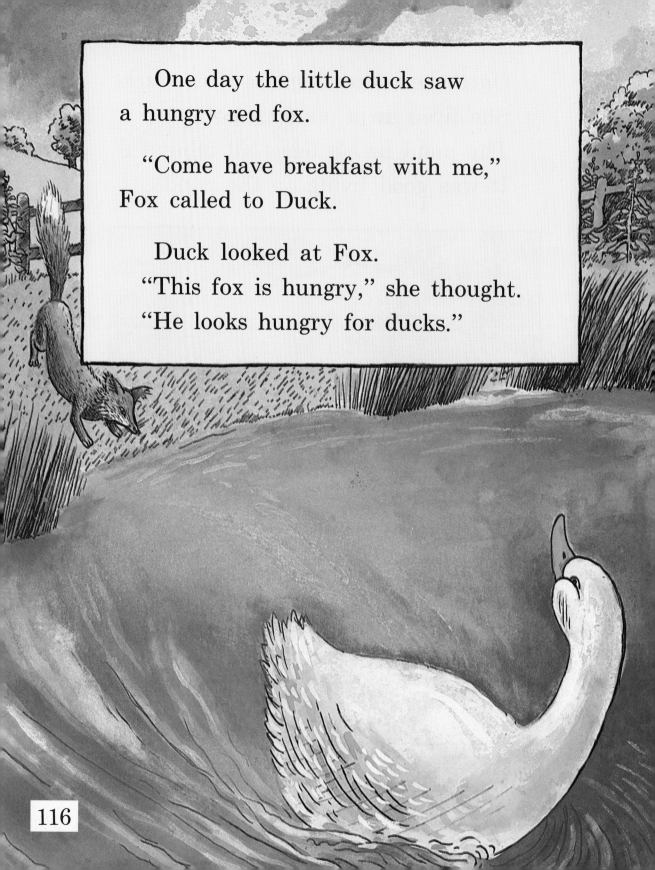

One day the little duck saw
a hungry red fox.

"Come have breakfast with me,"
Fox called to Duck.

Duck looked at Fox.
"This fox is hungry," she thought.
"He looks hungry for ducks."

So Duck asked, "How can we
eat breakfast without a table?"

"Wait there," called Fox.
"I will get a table."

Fox ran and ran.
He jumped over the fence.

Soon Fox came to a house.

He looked in the window.

No one was home, but he saw
a little table.

"No one needs this table now,"
thought Fox.

"I will take it."

The fox ran back to the pond
with the fence all around it.

"Here is a table," called Fox.
"Come have breakfast
with me, Duck."

"But I have had breakfast,"
called the little duck.
"Soon it will be lunchtime."

"Then come have lunch with me,"
called Fox.

He was hungry for duck
after all that running.

Duck said, "I need a plate
to put my lunch on.
How can we eat without plates?"

"Wait there," called Fox.
"I will get plates."

Fox ran and ran.

Soon he came to a house.

No one was home, but Fox saw
some plates on a table.

"I need plates," thought Fox.
"I will take what I need."

Then the fox ran back to the pond
with the fence around it.

"Here are the plates," called Fox.
"Come have lunch with me, Duck."

"I have had lunch," said Duck.
"Soon it will be supper time."

"Well then, come have supper with me," called Fox.

He was so hungry for duck after all that running.

The little duck asked, "How can we eat supper without a tablecloth?"

"If I get a tablecloth, *then* will you eat supper with me?" asked Fox.

"Yes," said Duck.

Fox ran and ran.
Soon he came to a house.
Fox saw a red tablecloth.

"I need that tablecloth," he thought.
"I will take it."

Fox ran back to the pond
with the fence all around it.

"Here's a tablecloth," called Fox.
"Come for supper, Duck."

"I want to see the tablecloth, Fox,"
called the smart little duck.
"I think it is too little."

"It's not too little," said Fox.
"Look!"

Then Fox saw why the pond
had a fence all around it.

Fox ran and ran,
and he didn't come back.

So once more it was good living
on the pond with the fence all around it.

Thinking It Over

Comprehension Questions

1. Why didn't Fox eat Duck?
2. What things did Duck ask Fox to get?
3. Fox ran and ran and didn't come back, so it was good living on the pond once more. Why?

Word Watch

What goes on a table?

a fence   a tablecloth

What goes on a tablecloth?

a plate   a table

What goes on a plate?

a pond   supper

What I Like to Eat

You know that Fox wanted to eat Duck for breakfast, lunch, and supper.

Make a book that shows what you like to eat for breakfast, lunch, and supper.

Show your book to your friends.

Ducks

by Mary Ann Hoberman

Ducks are lucky,
Don't you think?
When they want to
Take a drink,
All they do is
Duck their bill.
(Doesn't matter
If they spill.)
When they want to
Take a swim,
All they do is
Dive right in;
And they never
Seem to sink.
Ducks are lucky,
Don't you think?

Vowels a, e, i, and o

Vowels You Know

You know two sounds
for the vowel **a.**

Look at the words in the box.

Say the words and think about
the vowel sounds.

short a **long a**

back	made
name	
had	ran

Which words in the box
have a short **a** sound?

Which words have a long **a** sound?

You know two sounds
for the vowel **e** and two sounds
for the vowel **i.**

Say the words in each box.
Listen for the vowel sound
in each word.

short e

these	keep
let	
best	well

long e

Which words have a short **e** sound?
Which words have a long **e** sound?

short i

while	swim
if	
night	sign

long i

Which words have a short **i** sound?
Which words have a long **i** sound?

Another vowel sound that you know is the short **o** sound.

It is the vowel sound in **hot**.

Which of these things have names with the short **o** sound?

The Long o Sound

Now say the word **go**.

The vowel sound in **go** is the long **o** sound.

So, **coat**, and **go** all have the long **o** sound.

Which of these things have names with the long **o** sound?

Say the words in the box.
Listen for the vowel sound
in each word.

short o

box		nose
	not	
no		over

long o

Which words have a short **o** sound?
Which words have a long **o** sound?

Now you know the short
and the long **o** sounds.
Read what is in this box.

1. I will give him a **note**.
2. Give me the **mop**, please.
3. Did you **drop** your hat?
4. John went down the **road**.

My Dog
and the Key

by David A. Adler

Jennie thinks My Dog can find
lost things.
See if she can find a lost key.

My name is Jennie.
This is my dog.
I couldn't think of a good name
for her, so I named her My Dog.
My Dog is smart.
She can find lost things.

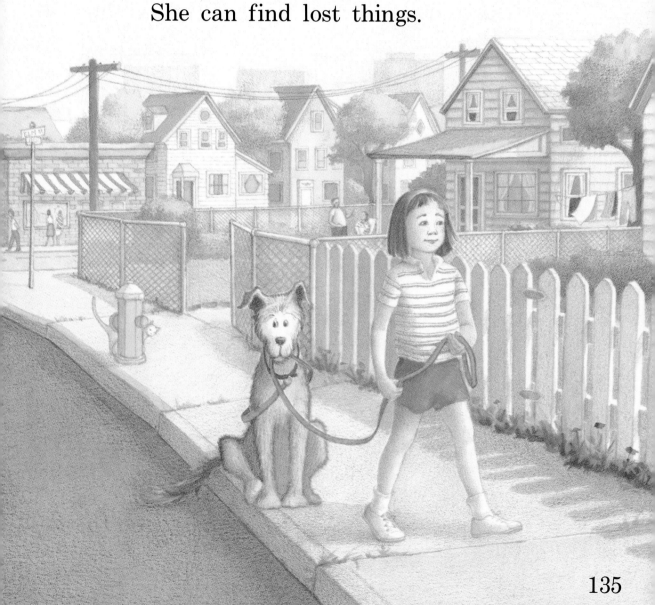

One day, My Dog and I
were by a tree.
We sat by the tree
for a long time.
It was a hot day.
But it was not hot by the tree.

My Dog pushed me with her nose.
She wanted me to take her
for a walk.

"Not now," I said.
"It's too hot."

My Dog pushed me some more,
but I still sat.

We were still at the tree
when Susan came by.

"I lost the key to my house!"
said Susan.
"My mother gave it to me today.
She said I am big now,
so I can have a key for myself.
But I lost it."

My Dog pushed me with her nose.

She wanted me to ask Susan more about the key.

So I asked her.

"I was in my house when my mother gave me the key," Susan said.

"But I don't know what I did with it."

This time I didn't wait for My Dog to push me.

"Take us to your house," I said.

"My Dog will find the lost key."

Soon we were at Susan's house.

Susan said, "I was here
when my mother gave me the key.
But now I know that I didn't
put the key down.
I had it when I went up to my room."

We went up to Susan's room.
Her things were all over the place.
I didn't want My Dog to go in there.
I didn't want her to get lost.

Susan said, "Now I know I didn't
put my key down in here.
I had it when I went to the kitchen."

My Dog pushed me with her nose.
"Let's go to the kitchen," I said.

Things were all over the kitchen.

"I was making biscuits," said Susan.
"I put the key here on the table."

There was no key on the table.

"Where did you roll out
the biscuit dough?" I asked.

"Here on the table," Susan said.

I started to think.

I thought about the key

and the biscuit dough.

"Oh, no!" said Susan.

My Dog was eating the biscuits.

"Stop it, My Dog!" Susan said.

"Stop eating all my biscuits."

"I know where your key is," I said.

"The key was on the table when you rolled out the dough," I said.

"You rolled the key up with the dough.

My Dog knows that.

She's eating your biscuits to find the key."

Susan didn't think My Dog wanted to find her key.

She thought My Dog was hungry.

But then we saw the key!

It fell out of a biscuit that My Dog
was eating.

It fell onto the table.

Susan thanked me for finding her key.

"Don't thank me," I said.
"Thank My Dog."

Susan started to thank My Dog,
but My Dog didn't look up.
She was still eating.

Thinking It Over

Comprehension Questions

1. How did My Dog find the lost key?

2. How did Jennie know the key would be in the biscuits?

3. Where can Susan put the key so it will not be lost again?

Word Watch

stop — start   **lost — found**   **ask — tell**

1. Dad said, "Please _____ singing.
   Mother is sleeping."

2. I _____ my lunch.
   Now I have something to eat!

3. What a good story!
   Please _____ it to me again.

Lost and Found

Tell about something you lost
and about how you found it.

Action Words

Tricks and Jolly play.
They run and jump.

Read these words.
play   run   jump

The words **play, run,** and **jump** tell
what Tricks and Jolly do.

Tricks ———— dog biscuits.
   hats   eats
Which word tells what Tricks does?

Jolly ———— over.
   rolls   boys
Which word tells what Jolly does?

Magazine Wrap-up

Looking Back

1. Duck, Marvin, and Jennie
each worked out a problem.
Tell about each problem
and how it was worked out.

2. Jennie said that My Dog was smart.
Do you think My Dog was smart? Why?
Was Freckles a smart dog? Why?
How about Tooley? Why?

I Would Like to Play With ___

Think about Jennie, Susan, Marvin, and Milton.

Which one would you like to play with? Why?

Books to Enjoy

Harriet Reads Signs and More Signs
by Betsy and Giulio Maestro

Signs help Harriet find her way all around town.

Roll Over   by Merle Peek

Some animals get in a bed one by one until there are too many!

Beware of a Very Hungry Fox
by Patty Wolcott

A hungry fox scares four chipmunks.

Parades
Magazine Three

Contents

Stories

Play

154

Willaby

by Rachel Isadora

Willaby gives a drawing
to Miss Finney, but she forgets
to sign it.

Will Miss Finney know who made
the drawing?

Willaby likes school.

She likes reading and counting.

She likes lunchtime.

She likes the children in her room.

She likes Miss Finney.

But Willaby likes to draw best.

When Miss Finney lets the children
decide what they want to do,
Willaby draws.

At home Willaby draws, too.

One day when Willaby went
to school, Miss Finney was sick.

Mrs. Benjamin said that Miss Finney
wouldn't be back to school for a while.

So the children decided to make
get-well cards for Miss Finney.

Then the children decided
to make up a poem for Miss Finney.
Mrs. Benjamin helped the children.
Soon the children were putting
the poem on the cards.

But not Willaby.
Willaby was drawing a picture.

Then Mrs. Benjamin asked
the children to give her the cards.

Willaby didn't know what to do.

She had not made a get-well card
for Miss Finney.

Now there was no time to make one.

Willaby decided to give her drawing
to Miss Finney.

On her way home that day,
Willaby thought, "I didn't put
my name on my drawing!
Now Miss Finney will not know
that I made something for her.
She may think I don't like her."

All the time that Miss Finney
was sick, Willaby made many cards
for her.

Willaby signed all the cards.

Soon it was the day for Miss Finney
to come back to school.

Willaby didn't want to go
to school that day.

She decided to take her time
and walk there.

At school, Willaby walked over
to her table without looking
at Miss Finney.

Then Willaby saw something
on her table.

Willaby didn't give Miss Finney
all the cards she had made.

She didn't have to!

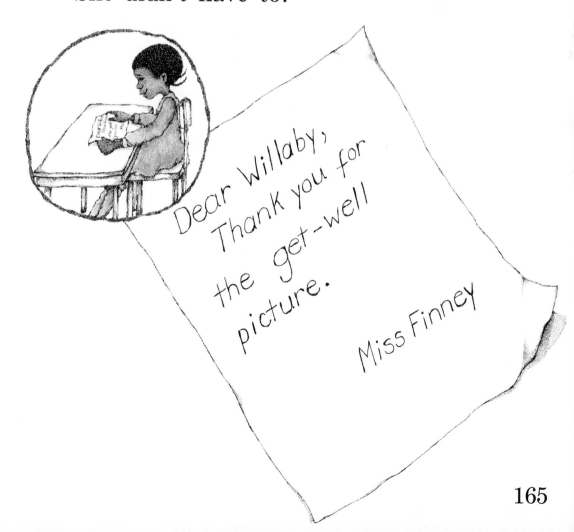

Dear Willaby,
Thank you for
the get-well
picture.

Miss Finney

Comprehension Questions

1. How did Miss Finney know
   that Willaby had made the drawing?
2. How did Willaby feel about going
   to school on the day that Miss Finney
   came back?
   Why did she feel that way?
3. Willaby liked to draw,
   but sometimes drawing isn't
   the best thing to do.
   Why not?

Word Watch

drawing   card   poem

These words name things that
you can make.
Make one of them for a friend.

What I Like to Do

Tell about what you like
to do best.

Johnny Drew a Monster

by Lilian Moore

Johnny drew a monster.
The monster chased him.
Just in time
Johnny erased him.

168

Who Helps Bear Cubs?

New bear cubs are so little.
They can't see well.
They can't get things to eat.
But they are cute!
When cubs are so little,
they do not go out.
The mother bear gives her cubs
all that they need.

Soon the cubs are not so little.
They go out with their mother.
Everything is new to the cubs!
They want to see everything.
The cubs have a good time
jumping, rolling, and playing.
Don't they look cute?

The mother bear is with her cubs
all the time.

She helps them find things to eat.

She helps them know all about
the things bears do.

Someday, when the cubs are big,
their mother will not need
to help them.

Thinking It Over

Comprehension Questions

1. What are new bear cubs like?
2. A mother bear will not help her cubs when they are big. Why not?

Word Watch

cute cubs   brown dogs   silly hats

Draw one of these things.

More About Bears

Tell about some of the things that the bear cubs did.

Find out about some other things that bears do and tell about them.

Naming Words

The words in the box name some animals you may find at a pond.

turtles   ducks   fish

Look at the picture.
Look at the naming words in the box.

Which animal name goes in each one of these to tell about the picture?

1. There is one _____ in the pond.
2. There are two _____ in the pond.
3. There are three _____ in the pond.

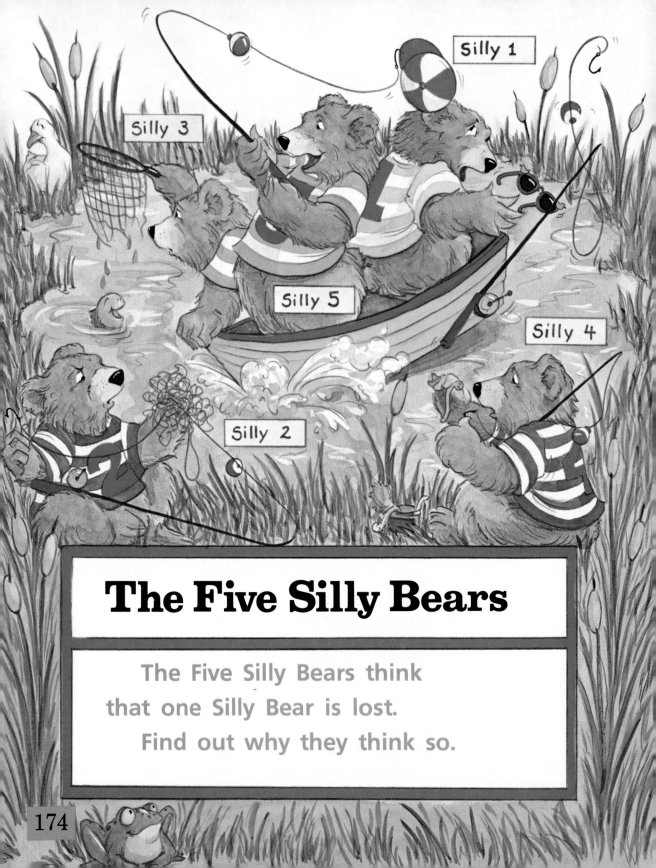

Silly 1

Silly 3

Silly 5

Silly 4

Silly 2

The Five Silly Bears

The Five Silly Bears think
that one Silly Bear is lost.
Find out why they think so.

Silly Five: I like being here
at the pond.

Silly Two: I do, too.
We have had fun.
But we came here to get some fish,
and not one of us could get one.

Silly Five: Now it's time to go home.

Silly One: Yes, it's getting dark.
It's so dark that I can't see
all of us.

Silly Three: I know that I am here.
Do you think that one of us fell
into the pond?

Silly Four: Yes, I think so!

Silly Five: Well, I don't think so.
I'll count us and see if one of us
is lost.
Here I go.
One, two, three, four.

Silly Three: Oh, no!
There were five of us when we came
to the pond.
You have counted only four.

Silly Two: We have lost a Silly Bear!

Silly Four: Boohoo! Boohoo!
One Silly Bear fell into the pond.
What are we going to do?

Silly Three: Maybe you didn't count every bear, Silly Five.

Silly Five: But I did!

Silly Three: Well then, who fell in?

Silly One: I didn't.

Silly Two: Look, here comes Fox. We can ask Fox for help.

Silly Four: No one can help us.
Boohoo! Boohoo!

Fox: Why are you crying, you Silly Bear?

Silly Four: One of us is lost, Fox.

Silly Three: We think that one of us
fell into the pond.

Silly Five: When we came here,
there were five Silly Bears.
Now we can find only four of us.

Silly One: We have to find
the lost Silly Bear.

Silly Two: We have to fish
that Silly Bear out of the pond.

Fox: Who did the counting?

Silly Five: I did.

Fox: Let me see you count,
Silly Bear Five.

Silly Five: One, two, three, four.

Silly Four: See, Fox?
   There are only four of us.
   Boohoo! Boohoo!

Fox: Stop, Silly Bear Four!
   There is nothing to cry about!

Silly Four: Nothing to cry about?
   Why not?
   Have you found the lost Silly Bear?

Fox: No one is lost.
   Look, I will count.
   One, two, three, four, five.

Silly Three: Five bears!
When Silly Five counted,
he counted only four bears.

Silly Five: Where did you find
the lost bear?
Did I forget someone?

Fox: You did forget someone, Silly Five.
When you counted, you did not
count yourself!

Silly Five: Oh, that was silly of me!

Silly One: Well, now that Fox showed
that we are all here, we can go home.

All the Bears: Thank you
for finding all of us, Fox.
Good-by!

Fox: Good-by, you Silly Bears.
And don't forget this, Silly Five.
When you count Silly Bears,
you need to count yourself, too!

Thinking It Over

Comprehension Questions

1. Was a Silly Bear lost?
   Why did the Silly Bears think so?
2. Who helped the Silly Bears?
   How did he help?
3. What do you think the Silly Bears
   would have decided to do if Fox
   had not helped them?

Word Watch

**one plate   two hats   three keys
four windows   five bears**

Draw pictures of these things.

Something Silly

The five bears were silly.
Tell about a time when you
did something silly.

What Will Happen?

Have a good day, Pam.

Think about what will happen next.

1. Pam will go to the store.
2. Pam will go to school.

What helped you to know that Pam
is going to school?

Here are some things that helped you.
Pam was taking books.
Gramps said, "Have a good day, Pam."

Read what is in this box.

> "We'll go to the pond
> after breakfast," said Dad to Lee.
> "We'll take our boat with us.
> We'll take some worms, too."

Where are Dad and Lee going?
1. They are going to the movies.
2. They are going fishing.

What helped you to know that Dad
and Lee are going fishing?

Thinking about both the boat
and the worms helped.

Thinking about the pond helped, too.

Were there any other things
that helped you?

Sometimes you can tell what
will happen next if you think about
what you have read and what you know.

Now read what is in this box.

Dad put a worm on Lee's fishing line.

Lee put the line into the pond.

Lee and Dad sat still.

Soon both of them saw something jump.

Then Lee's fishing line jumped.

What do you think happened next?
What helped you to know that?

Ira Sleeps Over

**story and
pictures by
Bernard Waber**

Ira is going
to sleep over
at Reggie's house.

Ira needs to decide
if he will take
his teddy bear.

If Ira takes
the bear, will Reggie
say that Ira is silly?

If Ira doesn't
take the bear, will he
miss it?

Find out what Ira
decides to do.

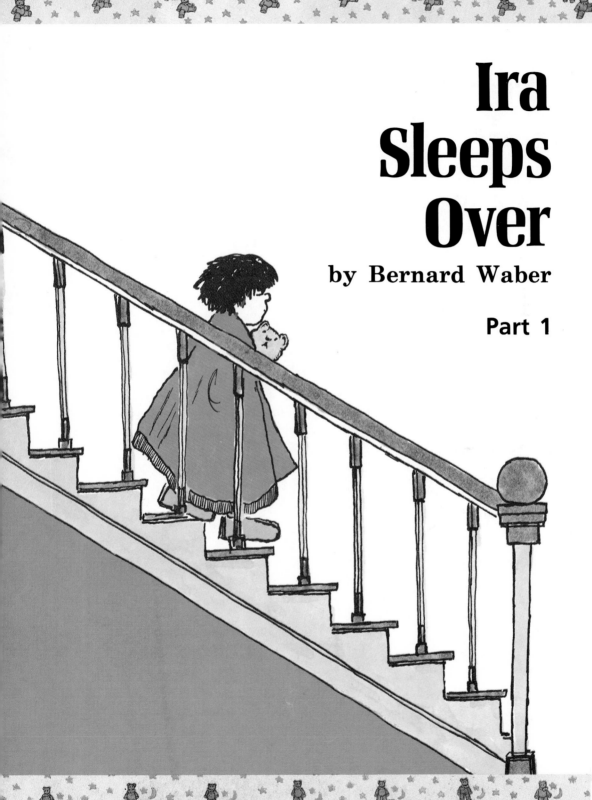

Ira
Sleeps
Over

by Bernard Waber

Part 1

I was going to sleep over
at Reggie's house.

It was going to be fun.

But I had a problem.

It was my sister who thought
of the problem.

She asked, "Are you taking
your teddy bear?"

"Taking my teddy bear!" I said.
"To Reggie's house?
No, I'm not taking my teddy bear."

And then she said, "How will it be
sleeping without your teddy bear?
Hmmmmmm?"

"It will be OK.
I'll like sleeping
without my teddy bear," I said.

But now she had me thinking
about it.
"What if I don't like sleeping
without my teddy bear?" I thought.
"Maybe I'll take him."

"Take him," said my mother.

"Take him," said my father.

"But Reggie will laugh," I said.

"He won't laugh," said my mother.

"He won't laugh," said my father.

"He'll laugh," said my sister.

I decided not to take my teddy bear.

After that I went to play
with Reggie.

Reggie said, "When you come
to my house, we are going
to have fun, fun, fun."

"Good," I said, "I can't wait."

"By the way," I asked, "what do
you think of teddy bears?"

But Reggie said nothing
about teddy bears.

"When you sleep over,
we'll tell stories," said Reggie.
"We'll tell ghost stories."

"Ghost stories?" I asked.

"Yes, ghost stories," said Reggie.

I thought about my teddy bear.

197

"Does your house get dark?" I asked.

"Uh-huh," said Reggie.

"Very dark?" I asked.

"Uh-huh," said Reggie.

"By the way," I asked, "what do you think of teddy bears?"

But then Reggie had to go home. "See you," said Reggie.

"See you," I said.
I decided to take my teddy bear.

"Good," said my mother.

"Good," said my father.

But my sister said, "Will you tell Reggie your teddy bear's name? Did you think about how he will laugh at a name like Tah Tah?"

"He won't ask," I said.

"He'll ask," she said.

I decided not to take Tah Tah.

Thinking It Over

Comprehension Questions

1. What did Ira decide to do with his teddy bear? Why?
2. What made Ira think that taking his teddy bear would be a problem?

Word Watch

mother father sister

These are family words.
Draw a picture of a family.

I Like My _____

Ira liked his teddy bear.
Tell about something you like.

Ira Sleeps Over

by Bernard Waber

Part 2

It was time to go to Reggie's house.

"Good night," said my mother.

"Good night," said my father.

"Sleep tight," said my sister.

I went over to Reggie's house.

That night we played
with everything in Reggie's room.

Then Reggie's father said,
"Bedtime!"

"Now?" asked Reggie.

"Now," said his father.
"Sleep tight."

We got into bed.

"Now we can tell ghost stories,"
said Reggie.

"Do you know one?" I asked.

"Uh-huh," said Reggie.
"Once there was this ghost
who lived in a big, dark house.
And every night this ghost said,
Ooooh! Ooooooooooh! Like that."

"This ghost would go looking
for someone to scare," said Reggie.

"And the ghost was very scary
to look at.

Oh, was it scary to look at!"

Reggie stopped.
"Are you scared?" he asked.

"Uh-huh, are you?" I asked.

"What?" asked Reggie.

"Are you scared?" I asked.

205

"Wait," said Reggie.
"I have to get something."

"What is it?" I asked.

"Oh, something," said Reggie.

Reggie got the something out.
The room was dark, but I
could see what he had.
It looked like a teddy bear.
I looked some more.
It *was* a teddy bear.

Reggie got back into bed.
"Now, about the ghost ... " he said.

"Is that your teddy bear?" I asked.

"This teddy bear?" asked Reggie.

"Yes, that one," I said.

"Uh-huh," said Reggie.

"Do you sleep with it
all of the time?" I asked.

"Uh-huh," said Reggie.

"Does your teddy bear
have a name?" I asked.

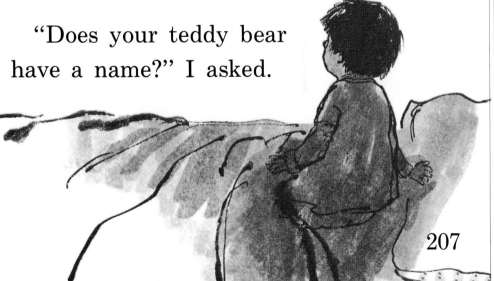

"You won't laugh?" asked Reggie.

"No, I won't laugh," I said.

"It's Foo Foo," said Reggie.

"Foo Foo?" I asked.

"Uh-huh," said Reggie.

"I have to get something," I said.

"What do you have to get?" asked Reggie.

"Oh, something," I said.

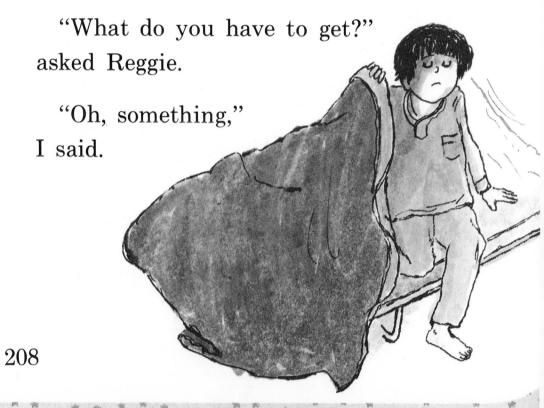

I went back to my house.

"Ira!" everyone said.
"What are you
doing here?"

"I decided to take
Tah Tah," I said.

I went up
to my room.
I came back
with Tah Tah.

My sister said,
"Reggie will laugh."

"He won't laugh," said my mother.

"He won't laugh," said my father.

"He won't laugh," I said.

I came back to Reggie's room.
"I have a teddy bear, too," I said.
"Do you want to know his name?"

I waited, but Reggie said nothing.
I looked at Reggie.
He was sleeping.

"Reggie!" I said.
"You have to tell the ghost story!"
But Reggie went on sleeping.

And after that —
There was nothing to do after that.

"Good night," I said to Tah Tah.
And I went to sleep, too.

Comprehension Questions

1. Did Ira take Tah Tah
   to Reggie's house? Why?

2. Why hadn't Reggie said anything
   to Ira about Foo Foo?
3. How will Reggie find out
   that Ira has a teddy bear?
   Do you think that Reggie
   will be surprised? Why?

Word Watch

Jed won't go to see _____ movies.
scary   orange

I laugh at _____ stories.
hungry   silly

Ana looked out at the _____ night.
dark   cute

The Story I Like Best

Ira and Reggie liked ghost stories.
Tell the name of a story that you like, and tell why you like it.

My Teddy Bear

by Marchette Chute

A teddy bear is a faithful friend.
You can pick him up at either end.
His fur is the color
   of breakfast toast,
And he's always there
   when you need him most.

Magazine Wrap-up

Do You Remember?

1. What were Willaby, the Silly Bears, and Ira each scared of?

2. You have read about three kinds of bears.
   Tell about each kind.

Willaby Makes a Drawing for Ira

If Willaby made a drawing
for Ira, what would it look like?
Make the drawing or tell about it.

Books to Enjoy

Gone Fishing   by Earlene Long
Father and his little boy go fishing.
Find out who gets a big fish.

Little Bear   by Else Minarik
Here are four good stories about
Little Bear and Mother Bear.

It's Not Easy Being a Bunny
by Marilyn Sadler
A rabbit wants to be a bear or a pig.
He wants to be anything but a rabbit!

Reading Helps

Sounds You Know

b c d f g h j k l m n p r s t v w x y

ch 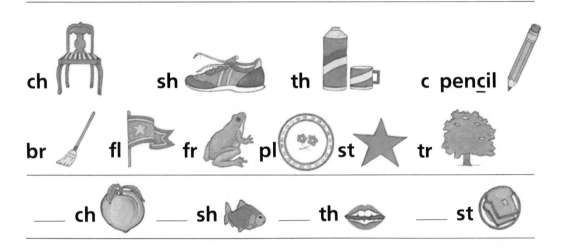 sh th c pencil

br fl fr pl st tr

___ ch ___ sh ___ th ___ st

short **a**   long **a**
can   am   make   take

New Sounds

kn sc ___ ck

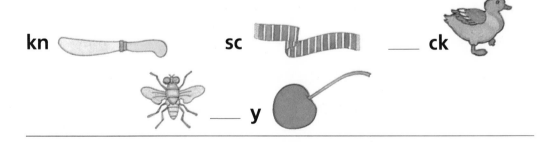

___ y

More New Sounds – Vowels

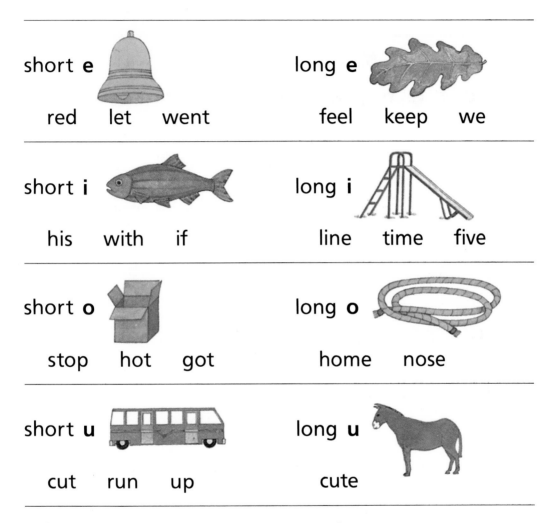

short **e**	long **e**
red let went	feel keep we
short **i**	long **i**
his with if	line time five
short **o**	long **o**
stop hot got	home nose
short **u**	long **u**
cut run up	cute

When you come to a new word –
Read to the end of the sentence.
Think about what the words are saying.
Think about the sounds for letters.

Credits